HUGGING THE JUKEBOX

HUGGING THE JUKEBOX

Naomi Shihab Nye

The National Poetry Series ✧ Selected by Josephine Miles

E. P. Dutton · New York

For
    Miriam and Aziz Shihab,
        Nina and Paul Nye,
            with enormous love

For information contact:
E. P. Dutton, Inc.
2 Park Avenue, New York, N. Y. 10016

Library of Congress Cataloging in Publication Data

Nye, Naomi Shihab.
  Hugging the jukebox.

  (The National poetry series)
  I. Title. II. Series.
PS3564.Y44H8 1982   811'.54   81-12583
                                          AACR2
ISBN: 0-525-24116-7 (cl)
      0-525-47703-9 (pa)

*Published simultaneously in Canada by Clarke, Irwin & Company Limited, Toronto and
Vancouver*

Designed by Kingsley Parker

10   9   8   7   6   5   4   3   2   1

First Edition

Contents

ACKNOWLEDGMENTS

I would like to thank the editors of the following magazines in which these poems previously appeared:

Affinities: "The Mother Writes to the Murderer: A Letter";
   "Envy"; "Getting Through the Day"; "The Trashpickers,
   Madison Street."
Alembic: "Sleeping in a Cave."
Cedar Rock: "At the Fair in Chimaltenango"; "Talk."
Cellar Door: "Making a Fist."
Chawed Rawzin: "The Barber."
En Passant: "Chula."
Impact: "The Flying Cat."
Kalliope: "So Much Happiness"; a longer version of "The Shapes of Mouths at
   Parties."
Loon: "On Counting Chickens."
Nethula Journal of Contemporary Literature: "First Things Last."
permafrost: "The Song."
The Pontchartrain Review: "For Lost and Found Brothers"; "Lights
   from Other Windows"; "For Rose on Magnolia Street."
Puerto del Sol: "One Island."
riverSedge: "Sleeping and Waking."
Shadowgraphs: "Another Vegetable Truck, 1980"; "The Passport
   Photo"; "Touring Mexico with Two Bird Watchers"; "Living
   in a Hundred-Year-Old House"; "Father Joseph and the
   Green Wool Coat."
Texas Portfolio Press: "Nelle."

Ten poems first appeared in *On the Edge of the Sky,* a chapbook published by Iguana
   Press (Madison, Wisconsin, 1981).

1

For Lost and Found Brothers

Where were you in winters of snow,
what ceiling did you stare at
before the dark came home to hold your hand?
What did your mama tell you about the world?

Facts interest me less than the trailing smoke of stories.
Where were you when no one else was there?

You lived in France at the foot of mountains
with paper, with creamy white days.
You hiked railroad tracks dreaming of mirrors,
how one life reflects another, goes back and back and back.
You stood in rooms, your black eyes birds barely landed,
and learned the long river that was your voice.
Thank you, a stone thrown in, a stone quietly sinking.
Thank you, a ripple returned.
So today when you bend to sign the first page of your book
there are other things to thank too,
the days folded behind you, in your wake,
this day connected, more mirrors, more birds.

For you, brothers.
For the blood rivers invisibly harbored.
For the grandfathers who murmured the same songs.
And for the ways we know each other years before meeting,
how strangely and suddenly, on the lonely porches,
in the sleepless mouth of the night,
the sadness drops away, we move forward,
confident we were born into a large family,
our brothers cover the earth.

Lights From Other Windows

Driving west tonight, the city dissolves behind us.
I keep feeling we're going farther than we're going,
a journey that started in the deep inkwell
out of which all our days are written.
Nothing is said to indicate a monument,
yet I perch on the edge of some new light.
The hills could crack open and a pointed beam,
like the beams on miners' hats, could pick us off this road.
Signals blinking, we arrive in a bright room
of greetings and hands. But when the stories spill,
I feel myself floating off alone into that night we just left,
that cool black bag of darkness, where black deer
nibbled invisible grasses and black fences divided one thing
from the next. A voice in my earliest ears *not this, not this*
and the lit windows of childhood rise up,
the windows of houses where strangers lived,
light slanting across black roads,
that light which said *what a small flicker is given
to each of us to know*. For seconds I dreamed their rooms
and tables, was comforted by promise of a billion other lives.
Like stars. Like knowing the Milky Way
is made of more stars than any naked eye can count.
Like having someplace to go when your glowing restlessness
lifts you out of rooms, becomes a wing,
takes you farther than you will have traveled
when your own life ends.

At the Seven-Mile Ranch, Comstock, Texas

I live like I know what I'm doing.

When I hand the horses a square of hay,
when I walk the road of stones
or chew on cactus pulp,
there's a drumming behind me,
the day opens up to let me pass through.

I know the truth,
how always I'm following each small sign that appears.
This sheep that materialized behind a clump of cenizo bushes
knows I didn't see him till he raised his head.

Out here it's impossible to be lonely.
The land walking beside you is your oldest friend,
pleasantly silent, like already you've told the best stories
and each of you knows how much the other made up.

Daily

These shriveled seeds we plant,
corn kernel, dried bean,
poke into loosened soil,
cover over with measured fingertips

These T-shirts we fold into
perfect white squares

These tortillas we slice and fry to crisp strips
This rich egg scrambled in a gray clay bowl

This bed whose covers I straighten
smoothing edges till blue quilt fits brown blanket
and nothing hangs out

This envelope I address
so the name balances like a cloud
in the center of the sky

This page I type and retype
This table I dust till the scarred wood shines
This bundle of clothes I wash and hang and wash again
like flags we share, a country so close
no one needs to name it

The days are nouns: touch them
The hands are churches that worship the world

The Lost Parrot

Carlos bites the end of his pencil
He's trying to write a dream-poem, but waves at me, frowning

     I had a parrot

He talks slowly, like his voice travels far
to get out of his body

     A dream-parrot?
     No, a real parrot!
     Write about it

He squirms, looks nervous, everyone else is almost finished
and he hasn't started

     It left
     What left?
     The *parrot*

He hunches over the table, pencil gripped in fist,
shaping the heavy letters
Days later we will write story-poems, sound-poems,
but always the same subject for Carlos

     It left

He will insist on reading it and the class will look puzzled
The class is tired of the parrot

     Write more, Carlos
     I can't

     Why not?

     I don't know   where   it went

Each day when I leave he stares at the ceiling
Maybe he is planning an expedition
into the back streets of San Antonio
armed with nets and ripe mangoes
He will find the parrot nesting in a rain gutter
This time he will guard it carefully, make sure it stays

Before winter comes and his paper goes white
in all directions

Before anything else he loves
gets away

The Teacher's Lounge

She speaks and my ears curl up
like dogs in a corner.

I scold myself, this is not like you,
you love people, ten minutes ago
the wind was in your hair.

Sometimes the world balloons emptily.
Cups are lifted and set down.
What could have been a tale
sharp as an Indian's arrow,
tumbles around the room
like any thrown twig.
The dog in my ears can't rise
to bring it back.

Where Children Live

Homes where children live exude a pleasant rumpledness,
like a bed made by a child, or a yard littered with balloons.

To be a child again one would need to shed details
till the heart found itself dressed in the coat with a hood.
Now the heart has taken on gloves and mufflers,
the heart never goes outside to find something to ''do.''
And the house takes on a new face, dignified.
No lost shoes blooming under bushes.
No chipped trucks in the drive.
Grown-ups like swings, leafy plants, slow-motion back and forth.
While the yard of a child is strewn with the corpses
of bottle-rockets and whistles,
anything whizzing and spectacular, brilliantly short-lived.

Trees in children's yards speak in clearer tongues.
Ants have more hope. Squirrels dance as well as hide.
The fence has a reason to be there, so children can go in and out.
Even when the children are at school, the yards glow
with the leftovers of their affection,
the roots of the tiniest grasses curl toward one another
like secret smiles.

Martita y Luisa

1.

Martita, a carriage of windows is passing by!

Aye, aye, little sister,
tomorrow they will all be closed.
You will sing me the song
of the folded bug.

Martita, the river is crayons,
the color blue will make me a boat!

And it will sink, little sparrow,
there are holes in the bottoms of boats
that are wider than our names. Even a name
like Martita.

2.

All day they spin marbles among stones.

Who is the street-sweeper?
Where does he sleep from morning till night?

He lives in a shadow room.
His mouth is the moon that is almost gone.

Where does the mailman put down his bag?

In the cemetery, on the grave of a child
who never learned to read or write.

Why does the Chinese woman
with a bandanna knotted on her head
push a cartload of cabbages
six miles every day?

They will wilt if she does not get there.

But where? Where is she going
in the sun, in the rain?

Now you come to the question made of ice.
It melts if I tell you.
Better to keep a few things floating,
a few things for the future,
little sister, your turn.

3.

A marble blue as a birthday sky
swallowed by grass.

You were born before me.
Does that mean you die first too?

At the hour when mothers scrabble in cupboards
tilting the jars of oil,
light falls down among trees
like an old washed sheet.
All night it will be drying
in the cracks where lives come together,
where things are lost and never claimed.
Each sister thinks the other has it
in her pocket. Goodnight little world
of lizards, as they brush the hair,
as they snap the gowns they will wear
into the other country, pulling each other
by long long hands.

Irene

Irene, your bones are made of rain.
This is my baby sister, you say.
This is my cousin. This is my front porch.
You dreamed a blue bicycle
waited for you out front like a horse.

I want to give you a rose with a fat heart
that never stops blooming.
A house with window screens.
A cat with an endless purr.

Look at her, you say, she is dancing.
When you speak, a pool of whispers,
smaller than the lantana petals on the sidewalk.

Your sister stinks, Irene.
She needs a new diaper.
Your cousin's teeth are rotting out of his mouth.
This life you live in, carpet scrap on a crooked porch.

Where are your brothers, mis amigos,
the ones who hit you that day in my car?
Out shining shoes.
The pool has one wave. You told me this before.

A police car passes
and you say how he will raise his hand.
With the palm flat out, as if he is pressing against you.
It is a dry season, Irene,
heat wave, we have broken all the records.
I want to drag you to a harbor of boats.

This broken step, this slot of weeds.
I see the television, you whisper,
Programs no good, but they keep coming on.

Sometimes your eyes swerve sideways, your smile blurs.
A little girl, already a river.
Your cousin shows his muscle. He wants us to notice.
In your stories nothing can make him cry.

West Side

In certain neighborhoods
the air is paved with names.
Domingo, Monico, Francisco,
shining rivulets of sound.
Names opening wet circles
inside the mouth,
sprinkling bright vowels
across the deserts of
Bill, Bob, John.

The names are worn
on silver linked chains.
Maria lives in Pablo Alley,
Esperanza rides the Santiago bus!
They click together like charms.
O save us from the boarded-up windows,
the pistol crack in a dark backyard,
save us from the leaky roof,
the rattled textbook which never smiles.
Let the names be verses
in a city that sings!

For Rose on Magnolia Street

You ask me to take off my shoes
and it is correct somehow,
this stripping down in your presence.
Do you recognize in me
a bone, a window, a bell?

You are translating a child's poem
about the color gray.
I float through your rooms,
peeking at titles, fingering the laces
you drape from your walls.

The first place I visited you,
a tree grew out of your bedroom,
hole cut in the ceiling.
Today there are plants in your bathtub.
Their leaves are thick and damp.

I want to plant myself beside you
and soak up some of your light.
When the streetlamps cross their hands,
when the uncles shuffle home from the market
murmuring of weather and goats,
you lean into a delicate shawl,
the letters people write you
begin glowing in your baskets.
Yesterday you wrote of the dog-man
who wanders everywhere
followed by a pack of seven hounds.
Soon you will tell us the secret
behind our grandmothers' soft hair.

The Trashpickers, Madison Street

On the edge of dawn's pale eye,
the trashpickers are lifting the lid of every can,
poking inside with bent hanger and stick.
They murmur in a language soft as rags.
What have we here?
Their colorless overcoats drift and grow wings.

They pull a creaking wagon, tinfoil wads, knotted string,
to the cave where sacraments of usefulness are performed.
Kneel to the triple weddings of an old nail.
Rejoice in the rebirth of envelopes.
The crooked skillet finds its first kingdom
on a shelf where nothing is new.

They dream small dreams, furry ones,
a swatch of velvet passed hand-to-hand.
Their hearts are compasses fixed to the ground
and their love, more like moss than like fire.

Rebellion Against the North Side

There will be no monograms on our skulls.
You who are training your daughters to check for the words
"Calvin Klein" before they look to see if there are pockets
are giving them no hands to put in those pockets.

You are giving them eyes that will find nothing solid in stones.
No comfort in rough land, nameless sheep trails.
No answers from things which do not speak.

Since when do children sketch dreams with price tags attached?
Don't tell me they were born this way.
We were all born like empty fields.
What we are now shows what has been planted.

Will you remind them there were people
who hemmed their days with thick-spun wool
and wore them till they fell apart?

Think of darkness hugging the houses,
caring nothing for the material of our pajamas.
Think of the delicate mesh of neckbones
when you clasp the golden chains.
These words the world rains back and forth
are temporary as clouds.
Clouds? Tell your children to look up.
The sky is the only store worth shopping in
for anything as long as a life.

Nelle

For Nelle Lucas
1912 – 1976

1.

Around us the world sloped
into darkness.
Sound lost its shape,
became a pocket nothing could fill.
Sometimes I feared
those Texas hill country nights
were too wide, too empty,
the deer could be a hundred miles away.
Shhh, you'd say,
teaching me endless
choreographies of patience.
Then I'd see them, lean and angular,
loping up through mesquite
to the salt block, on time.
They moved carefully,
exacting their delicate presence
like a breath.
One, two, six deer,
there always seemed to be
another one in the background.
I watched them and I watched you,
perched comfortably inside your world
where stones had names
and plants had histories
and nothing could ever be lost.

2.

Nelle, your hands were earth,
whatever you touched was sifted,
made pure.

Somewhere you learned
lives could be fashioned like pots,
an Indian taught you,
hands rubbing canyons into clay.
Each movement you made,
an edge was smoothed.
Each day was a firing.
You squatted and stirred the coals,
patted your wholesome chapaties
till they puffed and browned.
Nelle, the ground you walked on
recognized your feet.
It sent you messages,
"When you get tired of your body,
come on home."

3.

Once you said you were scared of the dark.
I remembered this, months later, locking my city doors.
It seemed so strange. You, scared of anything.

The last time I saw you
I carried the darkness like a heavy coat
I didn't want to put on.

When I heard you were gone,
I dreamed of pots fired too high,
their glazes dripping.
I felt thin, stripped of something essential,
an animal without a winter fur.

Nelle, once we waited on a mountain
to hear the rocks sing.
This is what I want to remember,
their low voices, a humming of bone.

These are the stepping-stones
I use to cross the great distance.
I listen and hear what you were saying
With your language of feathers,
your plum jam verbs and ancient rhythms.
I pin them to our darkness
till there is no more fear.

Another Vegetable Truck, 1980

Sam Pedrazzi remembers the sharp breath of January mornings
when all doors swung open to his grandfather
and potatoes passed hand-to-hand.
There were more houses here,
chimneys with bricks stacked neatly
as corn on a cob. Yards of chickens
cackling at dawn. Sam's grandfather said
they saw ghosts, that's why they never
stopped talking. It was a world you tasted,
rich broth of dust and flame and skin.
A horse pulled the wagon then.

Eighty years later Sam hears it snort.
He steers his truck down sleepy streets
feeling his grandfather beside him.

> *Life will change, Sam, see, you got an engine,*
> *I told you life would change.*

But look here, celery still has leaves on one end only,
apples crack slick and hard in the palm.

> *The driveways under these dead leaves*
> *went to sleep years ago, Sam,*
> *they'll never wake up.*

But Sam, woolen cap pulled tight over his ears,
chooses what he hears.
You want an onion? He'll sell you a rotting onion
five times the grocery price.
Tell him that's too expensive? He'll throw in a curly pepper
to make you forget.

> When I was a baby
> a vegetable man named Henry

tossed me a tangerine,
first thing I ever caught.

And now, out of cool morning air which remembers everything,
Sam Pedrazzi comes rattling up Main Street
and I run out yelling greetings,
knowing I'll never get a bargain from Sam
yet when I buy from him,
I buy from his father and grandfather,
something perishable like childhood,
delicately balanced among fruits and leaves.

Chula

Tonight in your old room,
I picked up a blue matchbox
with three precise holes in the lid.
I opened it.
A fat metal sheep was sleeping in cotton.
I jumped when I saw it.
You gave me an odd look.

While this sheep sleeps,
you have sheared pastures,
dug your hands through vacant topsoil,
hit rock.
You let few people in.
Your eyes show white chips,
wool, bone, bits of winter.
It's hard to keep track of your address.

Months ago I found you, you found me,
it's hard to know.
I've been driving for years.
Until I saw this sheep
sometimes I wondered what kept me coming.

The Song

From somewhere
a calm musical note arrives.
You balance it on your tongue,
a single ripe grape,
till your whole body glistens.
In the space between breaths
you apply it to any wound
and the wound heals.

Soon the nights will lengthen,
you will lean into the year
humming like a saw.
You will fill the lamps with kerosene,
knowing somewhere a line breaks,
a city goes black,
people dig for candles in the bottom drawer.
You will be ready. You will use the song like a match.
It will fill your rooms
opening rooms of its own
so you sing, I did not know
my house was this large.

2

The Passport Photo

"The Passport Office welcomes photographs which depict the applicant as relaxed and smiling."

PASSPORT APPLICATION

Before they shoot, I think of where I am going,
Chile, the world's thinnest country,
the bright woven hats on the Indians of Peru.

I swallow the map of South America tacked to my kitchen door,
the swarm of strange names, blue rivers
like veins in an old woman's leg.

A continent I know little about, except what I have read
or my Bolivian neighbor's tales. "A School of Thieves,"
she tells me. "I'd stay home if I were you."

Trapped in front of the hot lights,
I try to forget distances,
how far I will be from the ones who loved me longest.

I do not think anything familiar or cozy.
I think coastlines, jagged edges, the roads ahead of me
cracking open like coconuts, and then I smile

Because this face you are snapping
is a map to another continent
I have barely begun to learn.

Touring Mexico with Two Bird Watchers

We wander after the bird watchers like two drugged parrots.
Stare through binoculars — nothing but cloud and blur.
Somehow we have missed the pale-winged Nun Birds
whispering in the tops of trees.

We tune more to civilization, proud men in black suits,
two sombreros asleep on a bench.
I have pledged myself to markets and shacks
while you were out seeking flower-vendors,
children tending dolls.
The eyes click into orbit, planets moved by color and light.

South of Matehuala, someone saw a Varied Solitaire
resting on a cactus fence. We saw the fence.

I hunger for detail, yet speak of animals
as if they were all one animal,
one large breathing below the surface of man,
one burrowing, one howl.
I gather shells without knowing what they are called in books.
If the bird watchers ask me what a bird looked like,
I answer, respectfully, "It had — wings."
And feel my ignorance rests somewhere close
to the heart of miracles.

This is the history of Mexico:
A tree splits under the beak of the Splendid Woodpecker.
A Mexican Flicker peacefully spins red wool with straw.
A Squirrel-Cuckoo trembles under the double weight of his name.
High in the mountains, villages composed of Least Antwrens
live happily. They do not know how powerful the other birds can be,
how the Solitary Eagle spreads his giant wings
to circle the lonesome earth.

Listen — tonight the bird watchers are tilting their ears
toward the jungle, the forest, the stars.
A Broad-billed Mourner is about to tell us
the latest episode of evening news
while we, gringos with brightly colored tents and no tail feathers,
peck and nest on the edge of the sky.

The Plaza at Muzquiz, Mexico

Cement benches engraved with the year, 1980.
The old benches have plodded off
like donkeys to lie down and die in some field.

Air engraved with the sweet slow passage
of families drifting home from La Feria
where they rode the rocket-ride
that turned them upside down
and met a pig with three pickled heads —

It was something to dress up for.

Now the babies are snoring,
faces smooth as ceramic cows.

The fountain sleeps
in its private memory of water.

On the road to Rosita
a fat bus is swaying dreamily like a weed.

This is the same plaza where an American once decided
he could be happy being a red popsicle
melting against a green popsicle
in the freezer
pushed by a clubfooted boy.

Making a Fist

"We forget that we are all dead men conversing with dead men."
JORGE LUIS BORGES

For the first time, on the road north of Tampico,
I felt the life sliding out of me,
a drum in the desert, harder and harder to hear.
I was seven, I lay in the car
watching palm trees swirl a sickening pattern past the glass.
My stomach was a melon split wide inside my skin.

"How do you know if you are going to die?"
I begged my mother.
We had been traveling for days.
With strange confidence she answered,
"When you can no longer make a fist."

Years later I smile to think of that journey,
the borders we must cross separately,
stamped with our unanswerable woes.
I who did not die, who am still living,
still lying in the backseat behind all my questions,
clenching and opening one small hand.

Clarence

We find him in the ruins,
pointing to a Mayan hieroglyph meaning "sky."
Later he speaks of birds,
a journey to track the mysterious Quetzal.

"There were three of them," he whispers, "nesting."
"We had traveled nine days through the jungle on a raft."

Behind him the trees weave together,
forget there are people who clear the land.
Clarence shows a jade amulet he pieced from slivers.
It fits the center of his black hand perfectly,
it was born there.

Where were you born? Vague trickles, Belize or Jamaica,
a childhood by the sea. His voice,
a music birds could answer, a man who has danced with animals
would have such a voice.

Where do you live? And Clarence sweeps his arm.
He has a covenant with this unmapped tangle,
the spaces between branches where light slides through.
He knows how long it takes to climb the Great Pyramid,
in leaps, without turning around.
No one has followed him, because no one can.
We dream of our bodies in space,
of dropping off the edge,
while deep in the jungles of the world
there are men who laugh,
who would gladly let go.

Tikal, Guatemala

At the Fair in Chimaltenango

An aged man with one eye swollen shut
sits cross-legged in the center of the street
waving a belt.

The belt is finely woven, pink and green stripes,
with a delicate fringe.

I stoop to ask the price.
He speaks one so reasonable I pay it instantly
in exact silver coins.

The man smiles, a grin so quick a fly couldn't land on it.

In the crowd of Indians pushing to the food stands,
our hands touch. I rise and move forward.

Later the Americans will ask me what I bought,
did I get a good deal.

Getting Through the Day

From the corners of the city
men are riding toward us on bicycles,
whistling happily.
It is evening.
The streets are ripe bananas.

Our hands had vocations
before they learned to peel and scrub.
No one had to teach them how to love,
where to touch.

This is the hiss the iron makes,
steaming the collars of shirts.
The men are bringing kisses,
a folded note describing our eyes.

It is the message the birds
click in the trees,
someone is coming,
there are people yet to meet
whose names are not written
in the world of the dead.

Guatemala City

One Island

When you meet a man who is satisfied with one island,
you want to walk around him, a complete circumference,
to find where his edges are. If there is sand
or reef — you want to see how the trees grow,
trapped in the wind. He shows you the spine
of a sea urchin nested in his foot.
This man whose soul is a boat tied to a single post —
you want to sit with him long enough
to hear the curled shell of your body whistling.
When you say ''California'' you are a space creature
talking about a star. Nothing grows there.
Here we have mangoes, purple sea-grapes,
hog-plums spilling ripe across a path.
He could show you where to dive to see caves underwater.
The sky is filled with people like you — halfway coming,
halfway going. A plane lands every day between five and six.
The islanders hear it, ears pressed to air,
the minute it leaves the shore. On cloudless days
the mountains of the mainland unfurl in the west.
Grocers write proud lists on blackboards beside their doors:
American Cheese, Canned Pork.
Inside are men counting pennies, suspenders ordered in 1968.
There's a lot to do here: walk, watch, breathe.
Yesterday the man found a hunk of driftwood
snagged in the swamp. Hired four friends to drag it out.
Today it becomes a woman listening.
The man drops his chisel, turns her so we can see all sides.
We dream of taking her home with us,
placing her away from the wall in a house far from water.
Why? Because she is like one island,
complete in herself, curves connected.
She only lets you go so far.

After that you are taking the chances
the pirates took, the chances you take every day,
when you live in a world that barely knows you
on a ship that is always pointed
somewhere else.

Honduras, 1980

The Stolen Camera

Since the camera was stolen,
everything is a photograph —
pink bloom against white stucco,
the serious face of the potato chip man
leaning over his cart.

In the square, gypsies with brilliant skirts
twirl among palm trees.
I reach for the camera, to hand it to you,
but it is gone, stolen by a thief
who knows nothing of lenses.

Are you thinking of the camera?
I ask you once,
and you nod.
You will not mention it.

Two days ago you snapped
the shriveled saint who kissed your hand,
the Twins of Bougainvillea laughing
in their windowsill.
Your camera had careful eyes,
and now the pictures are stolen inside it,
babies who will never be born.

How would I feel if they stole my pens?
My lips would go on making words,
when I crossed the dappled street,
words everywhere, like steps
or yellow leaves.

Today we pass the monastery silently.
Maybe we are soaking up light,
brief angles of sun on stone.

Maybe tonight when we sleep
all we have seen will arrange itself
inside us, quick trails of stars,
and we will wake glowing,
the world in our eyes.

Popayan, Colombia

The Austrians

Two of them, on a train in the Andes.
"The higher you go, the more you giggle."
In the mining camps, women wore hats like cupcakes.
Born above the tree line, their hearts had no leaves.
"Let's get off!" the Austrians said,
but the train was threading a steep gap
on a bridge like the bridges children draw.
If we fell, they would shake their heads in Lima
and use the papers to wrap a fish.
One Austrian said she had given up eating,
then bargained for a huge loaf from the next peddler that appeared.
She consumed the whole, in bits, carving it with a pocketknife.
I tell stories to myself, she said. Each night is a cave.
I paint stories on the walls.
Her friend had chocolate eyes and played the cello.
When llamas marked the slopes, ears knotted with purple yarn,
the Austrians rose up singing, Icicles! Broken bells!
Quick glass clappers against the window's solemn cliff!
We saw them twice afterwards, hauling sleeping bags out of trucks,
slicing mangoes at a cafe. Hello! Where will you be tomorrow?
And then they were gone with their songs
and someone else was riding that train.

Sleeping in a Cave

Our toes touched stone.
Above us, the seamless face of granite.
You slept, I floated inside
the sound of your breath.

In the distance the waterfall we had seen all day
roared down the mountain.
Steep trail, miles behind us,
white cow grazing on the edge of a cliff.

Who would find us in those peaks and clouds?
There on that continent where no one knew our names
we had claimed a deep hole, shelter from rain.
You lit two candle stubs while I stirred the thin soup.

Tomorrow we would climb farther, up to the second pass,
the burned-out slopes, the famous ruins.
We would lose ourselves again on that landscape
where any motion was swallowed by air.

I lay against you, thinking how fear presses circles under the skin.
How loneliness folds up to fit in a pack.
I thought about everything which means life and closed my eyes,
knowing I was as far away and as near to it as I would ever come.

The Inca Trail, Peru

The Indian Shirt from Ayacucho, Peru

Mapped hands smoothing the soft bowl of a spoon.
Had I ever been on an airplane,
she wanted to know,
had I ever been to Cuzco?
All my answers seemed smaller
than the loose skirt of her questions.
Spin this thread, she said,
but my hands were clumsy machines.
She said she could teach me.
Live here, we will show you how to make fires
in the shape of men's names.

Suddenly I was trying on shirts
like the one she wore, blue river,
a hole for the breast to come out
and pour into the baby's mouth.
Her braided friends gathered, chanting
She likes that one, She likes that one.

They would have sold me forty amulets,
pig's ear, dried rosemary, shrunken llama embryo,
to assure I would get what I wanted in life.

3

The Only Word a Tree Knows

Tonight the hens line up on a bamboo roost,
sides touching.
You can hold their evening in the palm of a hand,
wondering at restlessness,
the stranger people should never let in.

Pecans falling before we have cracked the ones from last year!
Squirrels building a nest under the roof!
There is nothing to do that isn't singular.
One meal, one letter, one memory roaring inside the head.

The trees promise to remember us.
Yes. It is the only word a tree knows.
Leaves dropping, it is the one thing left.

Tonight we will be branches loose in the wind of our bed,
a motion preceding and following everything we do.

The trees shrink on the wall of the sky.
Listen long enough, it sounds like
they're talking inside your head.
This bending, this rake —
a leaf lands, little boat, on the stair.
To be everywhere and know:
I was born to answer a tree.

Talk

We have traveled here like ringtail cats,
peering at one another out of the brush,
swallowing the stars with our eyes.

The fable of the giant bass comes up on a short line.
Tales of slapping the man who tried to kiss you
while you played the piano rise in old music,
a little out of tune.

We serve stories on a table wiped clean
by the lady whose husband spun off a horse
and will never speak again. Each of us using what he has
to make a road out of silence.

I tell of a man who planted his dream in the desert
and came home dressed like a priest.
You remember the girl with roses tattooed on her breasts,
and how she took your money to buy a wedding gown
and never paid you back.

In the next room your baby inhales deeply.
Soon she will chase the running shadow of a word.

The Shapes of Mouths at Parties

A mouth like a hammer
pounding out its own tale.
Sometimes I float among the mouths
carrying my own like an unpicked plum.
The man who tells about crashing in an airplane
does not need my "Oh really?" for his story to go on.
As if we were standing at some coast,
things continue without our help,
the predictable waves, the smooth-backed shells,
and the mouths like jellyfish swelling . . .
As if the mouth were the opening
most suited to knowledge and communication,
more than the weightless eye,
landing carefully on each occupied chair,
the fluent nose, vibrantly awake
before the mouth names what it is eating,
or the hand, the articulate hand,
which comes undressed to every party,
opens easily to receive wine or cake,
and secretly converses with the rug, the dog, the air.

On Counting Chickens

Not before they are hatched
No
And not after—
Chickens are capable of incredible tricks.
They may shock you.
They may vanish if you turn your back.
They may change their faces, trade beaks,
grow plumes, refuse to lay for weeks.
Not before, not after, not ever.

If you wonder what to do with this urge
to count, to make plans,
plan to do this:
count backwards until all numbers and feathers
are swallowed into a neat slow empty hole.
It can look like an egg.
It can be called zero.
Plan not to call it anything.
Do this whenever you need to forget.
You tried to count.
It did not work.
You need not wait till then.
Do this with a piercing kind of joy.

The Barber

Today I have cut the hair of two heads,
one I see frequently, which trails loneliness
in thick dark waves,
one I have never seen before
and will likely not see again,
though it was an interesting head
with gigantic eyeballs in the front.
I did not ask for the jobs.
They came at me with scissors.
Who did they think I am?

It was strange today, all of it.
Rain poured through the back door.
Lost women ate salads, the dishwasher cried.
I was ready to go home when everybody else
was ready for a haircut.
My life erupted in wild flashes.
Tom read the most intimate parts of his journal aloud.
The hair on the damp dim floor.

The Flying Cat

Never, in all your career of worrying, did you imagine
what worries could occur concerning the flying cat.
You are traveling to a distant city.
The cat must travel in a small box with holes.

> Will the baggage compartment be pressurized?
> Will a soldier's footlocker fall on the cat during take-off?
> Will the cat freeze?

You ask these questions one by one, in different voices
over the phone. Sometimes you get an answer,
sometimes a click.
Now it's affecting everything you do.
At dinner you feel nauseous, like you're swallowing
at twenty thousand feet.
In dreams you wave fish-heads, but the cat has grown propellors,
the cat is spinning out of sight!

> Will he faint when the plane lands?
> Is the baggage compartment soundproofed?
> Will the cat go deaf?

"Ma'am, if the cabin weren't pressurized, your cat would explode."
And spoken in a droll impersonal tone, as if
the explosion of cats were another statistic!

Hugging the cat before departure, you realize again
the private language of pain. He purrs. He trusts you.
He knows little of planets or satellites,
black holes in space or the weightless rise of fear.

Burning the Old Year

Letters swallow themselves in seconds.
Notes friends tied to the doorknob,
transparent scarlet paper,
sizzle like moth wings,
marry the air.

So much of any year is flammable,
lists of vegetables, partial poems.
Orange swirling flame of days,
so little is a stone.

Where there was something and suddenly isn't,
an absence shouts, celebrates, leaves a space.
I begin again with the smallest numbers.

Quick dance, shuffle of losses and leaves,
only the things I didn't do
crackle after the blazing dies.

Advice

My great-great-aunt says to plant a tree.
Any nut, she says. She says and says again.
She planted her tree in 1936.

Ahead of us the years loom, forests without histories.
Our hands want to plant something that will bloom tomorrow.
This is too vague, this deep root of ten thousand days.

Don't forget, she says, but we are driving away.
Behind us she brushes a leaf from her step,
sinks a little deeper into the soil of sleep
that has been settling beneath her like a pillow since birth.

Sleeping and Waking

1.

All night someone is trying to tell you something.
The voice is a harbor, pulling you from underneath.

Where am I, you say, what's this and who are you?

The voice washes you up on the shore of your life.
You never knew there was land here.

2.

In the morning you are wakened by gulls.
Flapping at the window, they want you to feed them.
Your eyes blink, your own hands are pulling you back.

All day you break bread into small pieces,
become the tide covering your straight clear tracks.

First Things Last

The kitchen cupboard was my shrine.
I sat cross-legged, removing skillets.

Mama would enter the room, hand to her ear.
Something she had forgotten, the name of a town,
a friend she wanted to call.
Landscapes swirled out from her fingertips,
but this was the Midwest, hopelessly flat and dry.

In my father's voice, a ship was pulling out from port.
Mama fed him lamb chops.
Her eyes were a package lost in the mail.

I wanted to tell them about the double boiler,
but this was before speech.
The way its sacred layers stacked together and fit,
in the cupboard in the corner,
by the mop and the broom.

Your Name

When I think of the years it took
for your name to build palaces
in the marrow of my smallest bones

How every journey uncurled
in the flannel pocket
where your name was sleeping

And the boats men found floating
after hurricanes had your name
carved in the sides

When I remember your name
as the peak on which I stood
to view the rest of the shining world

No wonder, when I heard it spoken today,
flipped into a conversation
like any other pennyworth word

I could not reply

It was not the same
name.

Famous

The river is famous to the fish.

The loud voice is famous to silence,
which knew it would inherit the earth
before anybody said so.

The cat sleeping on the fence is famous to the birds
watching him from the birdhouse.

The tear is famous, briefly, to the cheek.

The idea you carry close to your bosom
is famous to your bosom.

The boot is famous to the earth,
more famous than the dress shoe,
which is famous only to floors.

The bent photograph is famous to the one who carries it
and not at all famous to the one who is pictured.

I want to be famous to shuffling men
who smile while crossing streets,
sticky children in grocery lines,
famous as the one who smiled back.

I want to be famous in the way a pulley is famous,
or a buttonhole, not because it did anything spectacular,
but because it never forgot what it could do.

The Mother Writes to the Murderer: A Letter

"Alicia didn't like sadness."

THE DALLAS MORNING NEWS

To you whose brain is a blunt fist
pushed deep inside your skull
whose eyes are empty bullets
whose mouth is a stone more speechless
than lost stones at the bottoms of rivers
who lives in a shrunken world where nothing blooms
and no promise is ever kept

To you whose face I never saw but now see
everywhere the rest of my life

You don't know where she hid her buttons

arranged in families by color or size
tissue-wrapped in an oatmeal box
how she told them goodnight   sleep well
and never felt ashamed

You don't know her favorite word
and I won't tell you

You don't have her drawings taped to your refrigerator
blue circuses, red farms
You don't know she cried once in a field of cows
saying they were too beautiful to eat

I'm sure you never thought of that
I'm sure nothing is too beautiful for you to eat

You have no idea what our last words were to one another
how terribly casual

because I thought she was going a block away
with her brother to the store
They would be back in ten minutes

I was ironing her dress
while two houses away an impossible darkness
rose up around my little girl

What can I wish you in return?
I was thinking knives and pistols
high voltages searing off your nerves
I was wishing you could lose your own life
bit by bit   finger by toe
and know what my house is like

how many doors I still will have to open

Maybe worse would be for you to love something
and have it snatched up   sifted out of your sight
for what reason?
a flurry of angels recalled to heaven
and then see how you sit
and move and remember
how you sleep at night
how you feel about mail   my letter to you
all the letters passing through all the hands
of the people on earth
when the only one that matters
is the one you can neither receive
nor send

Living in a Hundred-Year-Old House

You could be the collection of marbles,
smoothness against smoothness,
in the flat wooden bowl.

The azalea gracefully losing petals
on the porch, the slight rain
sifting through the screen.

Perhaps the basket on the table
holding nothing but a wax apple
you keep waiting for someone to bite into
or the pottery duck with a cactus in its back.

You want little.
Only to know where every mind goes
when it is not with the feet,
what blossom it returns to again and again
to remind it this life is worth waking up for.

Noon.
Sometimes you feel yourself the way dust must feel itself,
drifting nameless, room to room.

Father Joseph and the Green Wool Coat

In your scrubbed white kitchen I made toast.
You talked hungrily, politics,
I nodded though I understood nothing.
Canadian villagers weren't very friendly, you said.

Mist rising off the lake —
I was leaving in an hour on a train to Halifax.
We ate jelly on our bread, it was like being
five years old at my grandmother's house,
everything so clean and quiet.
I felt when I walked out that door
no one would walk in it ever again
but you would keep sitting there, while the mist rose
and the trees got older and the silence thickened
like a lady's ankles under the table.

I had the feeling something was being given,
so when you handed me this jacket abruptly at the door
it was the gift after the gift,
the lace handkerchief passed down to the granddaughter
who already has her grandmother's eyes, hair, hands.

Envy

The cat on the chair
dreamily licks one paw

The white cat on the white chair
lives white minutes
I'm not even in

The Shopper

I visit the grocery store
like the Indian woman of Cuzco
attends the cathedral.
Repeating the words:
butter, bread, apples, butter bread apples.

I nod to the grandmothers
muttering among roots.
Their carts tell stories:
they eat little, they live alone.
Last week two women compared their cancers
matter-of-factly as I compare soups.
How do you reach that point of acceptance?
Yes and no shoved in the same basket
and you with a calm face waiting at the check-out stand.

We must bless ourselves with peaches.
Pray to the eggplant, silent among her sisters,
that the seeds will not be bitter on the tongue.
Confess our fears to the flesh of tomato:
we too go forward only halfway ripened
dreaming of the deeper red.

The Hat

"You gotta believe in something or the world's gonna blow up."
MARTIN BAROS, Shiner, Texas

At the Shiner auction, it's not hard to believe in
homemade noodles, ringtailed doves,
Riding on a Railroad quilts.

I can believe the ladies strolling by in knit pants
and cowboy boots have happy marriages
and no one in this town locks doors.

Martin bids on everything and flushes red under the sun.
A blue straw hat sits on his head like a flower.

All day people greet him,
Nice hat, Martin, nice hat.

It's my auction hat, he says proudly.
I only wear it to the auction,
then I save it for the next year.

That night, pedaling home,
I keep thinking about the box in his closet,
the hat going into the box,
the box waiting on the shelf
three hundred sixty-four more days.

Dog

The sky is the belly of a large dog,
sleeping.
All day the small gray flag of his ear
is lowered and raised.
The dream he dreams has no beginning.

Here on earth we dream
a deep-eyed dog sleeps under our stairs
and will rise to meet us.
Dogs curl in dark places,
nests of rich leaves.
We want to bury ourselves
in someone else's home.

The dog who floats over us
has no master.
If there were people who loved him,
he remembers them equally,
the one who smelled like smoke,
the one who brought bones from the restaurant.
It is the long fence
of their hoping he would stay
that he has jumped.

At Portales, New Mexico

For Frank and Kathy Cioffi

They spoke of tumbleweeds
coming to their doors in the night,
whole herds of them scooting across the desert,
arriving at any place there was a wall,
and staying.
In the morning they would rise
to find them stacked,
grazing on air.

Their neighbor tried fire
but his living room went up in flames.
You couldn't fit a tumbleweed in a garbage sack
unless it was a baby one.
If you swept them across the street
they would return to you, loyal,
on the next powerful gust.

What did people do to protect their houses
in New Mexico?
At night they dreamed eastern hedges guarded their beds,
steady lamplight palming each roof.
They never knew they would be planted
on this thin blue line,
nothing between themselves and the next town
but a sign for Indian Gifts.

Where they grew up a root meant something.
Trees lived a hundred years
and bulbs slept secure in the ground.
But here in the West,
the days were flat tables spread with wind,
you never knew who was coming,

how many places to set for dinner;
they had imagined a knock
and opened the door for four big ones,
rolling, right up to the chairs.
You never knew how far your voices would travel
once you let a word out,
felt that curled stem shrinking in your throat
and the thousand directions it could
or could not go.

So Much Happiness

For Michael

It is difficult to know what to do with so much happiness.
With sadness there is something to rub against,
a wound to tend with lotion and cloth.
When the world falls in around you, you have pieces to pick up,
something to hold in your hands, like ticket stubs or change.

But happiness floats.
It doesn't need you to hold it down.
It doesn't need anything.
Happiness lands on the roof of the next house, singing,
and disappears when it wants to.
You are happy either way.
Even the fact that you once lived in a peaceful tree house
and now live over a quarry of noise and dust
cannot make you unhappy.
Everything has a life of its own,
it too could wake up filled with possibilities
of coffee cake and ripe peaches,
and love even the floor which needs to be swept,
the soiled linens and scratched records . . .

Since there is no place large enough
to contain so much happiness,
you shrug, you raise your hands, and it flows out of you
into everything you touch. You are not responsible.
You take no credit, as the night sky takes no credit
for the moon, but continues to hold it, and share it,
and in that way, be known.

Hugging the Jukebox

On an island the soft hue of memory,
moss green, kerosene yellow, drifting, mingling
in the Caribbean Sea,
a six-year-old named Alfred
learns all the words to all the songs
on his grandparents' jukebox, and sings them.
To learn the words is not so hard.
Many barmaids and teenagers have done as well.
But to sing as Alfred sings —
how can a giant whale live in the small pool of his chest?
How can there be breakers this high, notes crashing
at the beach of the throat,
and a reef of coral so enormous only the fishes know its size?

The grandparents watch. They can't sing.
They don't know who this voice is, trapped in their grandson's body.
The boy whose parents sent him back to the island
to chatter mango-talk and scrap with chickens —
at age three he didn't know the word "sad"!
Now he strings a hundred passionate sentences on a single line.
He bangs his fist so they will raise the volume.

What will they do together in their old age?
It is hard enough keeping yourself alive.
And this wild boy, loving nothing but music —
he'll sing all night, hugging the jukebox.
When a record pauses, that live second before dropping down,
Alfred hugs tighter, arms stretched wide,
head pressed on the luminous belly. "Now!" he yells.
A half-smile when the needle breathes again.

They've tried putting him to bed, but he sings in bed.
Even in Spanish — and he doesn't speak Spanish!
Sings and screams, wants to go back to the jukebox.
O mama I was born with a trumpet in my throat
        spent all these years tryin' to cough it up . . .

He can't even read yet. He can't *tell time*.
But he sings, and the chairs in this old dance hall jerk to attention.
The grandparents lean on the counter, shaking their heads.
The customers stop talking and stare, goosey bumps surfacing on their arms.
His voice carries out to the water where boats are tied
and sings for all of them, *a wave*.
For the hens, now roosting in trees,
for the mute boy next door, his second-best friend.
And for the hurricane, now brewing near Barbados —
a week forward neighbors will be hammering boards over their windows,
rounding up dogs and fishing lines,
the generators will quit with solemn clicks in every yard.

But Alfred, hugging a sleeping jukebox, the names of the tunes gone dark,
will still be singing, doubly loud now, teasing his grandmother,
"Put a coin in my mouth!" and believing what she wants to believe;
this is not the end of the island, or the tablets this life has been
scribbled on, or the song.

                               Utila, Honduras, 1980

The National Poetry Series
Third Annual Series — 1982

WINNERS OF THE OPEN COMPETITION:

Jonathan Aaron, *Second Sight* (Selected by Anthony Hecht)
Denis Johnson, *The Incognito Lounge* (Selected by Mark Strand)

OTHER WINNERS:

Cyrus Cassells, *The Mud Actor* (Selected by Al Young)
Naomi Shihab Nye, *Hugging the Jukebox* (Selected by Josephine Miles)
Sherod Santos, *Accidental Weather* (Selected by Charles Wright)